Follow Jesus

A Christian Teen's Guide to Navigating the Online World

Christine Carter

GROUND TRUTH PRESS

NASHUA, NEW HAMPSHIRE

Follow Jesus*:*
A Christian Teen's Guide to Navigating the Online World

Copyright © 2019 Christine Carter

Published by GROUND TRUTH PRESS
        P. O. Box 7313
        Nashua, NH 03060-7313

Editor: Bonnie Lyn Smith

Cover design: Michelle Fairbanks, Fresh Design

First printing 2019

Printed in the United States of America

Trade paperback ISBN-13: 978-1-7337677-0-5
Trade paperback ISBN-10: 1733767703

This book is dedicated to all the Christian teens who are trying their best to remain faithful in their walk with the Lord amidst the incredible obstacles they face along their path.

The internet is filled with opportunities that will test your faith and challenge you to demonstrate what it means to truly **Follow Jesus**.

May this guide strengthen your relationship with Jesus and instill the love, grace, humility, compassion, truth, wisdom, integrity, and faithfulness you need to navigate the online world.

Acknowledgments

This book was inspired by Galit Breen. She saw the need for a biblically based online guide for teens and asked me to meet it. She is the bestselling author of *Kindness Wins*: *A Simple, No-Nonsense Guide to Teaching Our Kids How to Be Kind Online*, and she offers the online courses: *Boom, Done, Digital Parenting*™ and *Raise Your Digital Kid*™. You can find all her work and services at <u>theselittlewaves.net</u>.

Table of Contents

Dear Teen,

I'm so glad you opened this workbook to learn more about Jesus and what it means to follow Him in the online world! I know there are many other things you could be doing with your time, and I'm thrilled you are making the important choice to grow in your faith and discover new ways to honor Christ when your fingers touch those screens!

I realize that perhaps this workbook was given to you and you may not have a choice in the matter. If that's the case, can you do me a favor and give it a chance? I've learned that God can do miraculous things with the smallest of steps, so please take a tiny step into this workbook with an open heart, okay? I think you'll be surprised that it's actually pretty helpful if you can take the time to work through it.

Surely, most teens spend time online, right? I'm guessing you have a phone and that it's pretty much attached to your hand regularly. Awesome. Your screen time is an incredible way to connect with the world and learn so much about it! You use your phone to watch your favorite shows and YouTube channels, and listen to your music, right? It's certainly an important way to interact with friends on social media and peek into other people's lives. I totally get that. I'm absolutely for it.

Don't think that this book is going to keep you *from* your phone, but, rather, think of it as a guide in *how to use it* as a Christian. There are no big surprises here. The goal of this book is to help you understand who Jesus is and how to apply the principles of your Christian faith to what you do and see online. Not scary at all! This book is only meant as *good* for you.

Okay?

Okay, then.

Let me start by asking you a few questions:

- When you are surfing the web for entertainment or information and find something you know God wouldn't approve of, do you take a look or click away?
- If you know something inappropriate or illegal is going around social media, do you engage in the hype, or do you block it and alert the authorities?
- When you are scrolling through your social media accounts, is your faith a factor when you are engaging with other people? Do you think about how God would want you to interact?

- When you are sharing posts and pictures on social media, are you constantly checking to see how many likes and comments you get? Do you measure your self-worth by that number?
- When you choose to follow people on social media, do you follow them because it's the popular thing to do, or are you careful about the people you place in your newsfeed?
- If you had an option to actually follow *Jesus* on social media, would you? Better yet, would you allow Him to follow *you*? Or would you be embarrassed if He saw what you share on social media and how you interact online?
- When your fingers touch the screen, do you remember that you are a Christian? Or do you forget who you are and *whose* you are when navigating the online world?
- And most importantly, if you chose to follow Jesus online, would you be willing to share what He shares? Would you be confident and courageous enough to promote His truth and His message to all who follow you?

Tough questions to answer, I'm sure.

Listen, you are at an age when these questions might seem discouraging and overwhelming. You might be realizing how you have failed and faltered in your faith. You might even think:

"How can I think about Jesus all the time in everything that I do?"

And I want you to know that you are not the only one who feels that way. You are not the only one who makes mistakes and forgets to uphold the very values you want to believe in. And also—you may not even be sure what you believe in anyway!

I know you have so much to worry about in your life and you likely feel so much pressure from many people. It can be really difficult to remember everything and be responsible ALL. THE. TIME. Am I right? Right. And adding more things to do and learn might seem intimidating, and you just aren't up for doing any more work.

But if you are reading this, I believe that deep within your heart, you have the desire to know God and you want to learn more about Jesus. God is tapping on your heart and calling you toward Him because He knows you are ready and willing to pursue and enrich your relationship with Him. You are reading this book for a reason. God handpicked YOU to be an ambassador for Christ online. He knows what you are capable of, and He gifted you with talents and skills that are extraordinary and unique to you. You are *so very special* and *so very loved.*

One thing I've learned as a Christian is that the more you get to know Jesus, the more you want to dive deeper into a relationship with Him! Who wouldn't want to be loved by the Creator of all things? And guess what? *You are.* The more you learn about this love, the more loved you will feel and the more you will want to share this undeniable love with others! Seriously, that's how it goes. That's why you see Christians who are madly in love with Jesus and are so passionate about sharing His love with other people. It's a pretty marvelous, miraculous thing, really. So, do me this small favor, and open your heart to this crazy love God has for you, okay? If all you do is that, I'll take it, and so will God. Baby steps become big steps in time with God. This I know for sure.

And one more great thing about God is that when we invite Him into our lives, we never have to do anything alone. All the challenges you face will be accompanied by your Heavenly Father who has the power to give you the strength and wisdom you need. If you can trust that God knows best and has **all** the answers, then doing hard things becomes possible. And there are *a lot* of hard things you are faced with as a teen. *I know.*

Please remember that through Christ, you are offered the full forgiveness of God, so let that truth be a comfort and encouragement to you as you grow in your faith. You will be challenged with many decisions online, and you might make mistakes. Please understand that Jesus won't ever abandon you. His mercies are new every morning! He will love you through *every single thing* you do. That's what's so amazing about our Heavenly Father. He never gives up on us! And He's always with us no matter how badly we screw up. There is no perfect Christian—we *all* mess up. The key to doing life with Jesus is your willingness, desire, and ability to accept the profound gift of grace that He offers you.

He doesn't expect you to be perfect. He knows you better than you know yourself, so He knows all your weaknesses and strengths—and all your hopes and dreams, too.

Isn't that amazing?

So, give Him a chance and this workbook a try, okay?

Now, let's get started.

Introduction

What does it mean to "Follow Jesus"?

When God created the earth and all living creatures in it, He had a perfect relationship with mankind. Then sin entered the world, which created a barrier between God and man. So, God came to earth, through His Son, Jesus Christ, to be sacrificed for all our sins, so He could reunite with His beloved children once again.

> To this you were called, because Christ suffered for you, leaving you an example, that you should follow in his steps.
>
> "He committed no sin, and no deceit was found in his mouth."
>
> When they hurled their insults at him, he did not retaliate; when he suffered, he made no threats. Instead, he entrusted himself to him who judges justly. "He himself bore our sins" in his body on the cross, so that we might die to sins and live for righteousness; "by his wounds you have been healed." For "you were like sheep going astray," but now you have returned to the Shepherd and Overseer of your souls. (1 Peter 2:21-25)

When we choose to follow Jesus, we accept Jesus Christ as our Lord and Savior, who washes us clean of all sin, so that we can be reconciled with our Heavenly Father.

> For God so loved the world that he gave his one and only Son, that whoever believes in him shall not perish but have eternal life. (John 3:16)

When we make this life-changing decision, we are given eternal life, and the Holy Spirit comes into our hearts to be God's Helper and Comforter. We have access to the perfect Trinity of God as Christians: God, the Father; God, the Son; and God, the Holy Spirit. After accepting Jesus as our Savior, we commit our lives to growing in Christ while learning more about who He is and how He wants us to live, according to God's Holy Word (the Bible).

If you haven't yet asked Jesus to be your Lord and Savior, you can say this prayer right now:

Dear Jesus,

I am so grateful that You died on the cross for my sins. I want to receive Your saving grace and invite You into my life as my Lord and Savior so that I can be cleansed of all sin and have eternal life. May Your Holy Spirit dwell in my heart as I follow You for the rest of my life.

In the name of Jesus, I am forever Yours,
Amen.

Following Jesus means we make choices every day that honor Christ who lives in us through the Holy Spirit; we do this through everything we say and do. It's not easy to live a life following Jesus because it's in our nature to sin, and sin interferes with our relationship with God and prevents us from growing closer to Jesus. God wants us to actively turn away from sin so that we can be fully connected to Him and experience the richness of our relationship with Him through Christ.

No one is perfect, so when we mess up, we are offered the gift of grace through Christ's sacrifice on the cross every time we come to Jesus with our sin and ask for forgiveness. But as we continue to follow Jesus, we will understand the extraordinary power of the Holy Spirit working in us, helping us draw on God's strength and wisdom to make godly decisions that honor Christ.

We can trust that our Lord is faithful in leading us on our God-given path that He created according to His purpose for our lives. When we choose to follow Jesus, we will be blessed with His abundant love, endless mercies, and newfound strength that only come through Christ.

To follow Jesus means we are to honor our Christian faith in everything we do, and we have the greatest opportunity and challenge to do this in the online world. The choices we make when we engage in social media are critical not only to our own relationship with Jesus but also to the people out there who watch us closely to learn what it *means* to follow Jesus. We are His ambassadors, and that is a mighty calling for us all.

> All this is from God, who reconciled us to himself through Christ and gave us the ministry of reconciliation: that God was reconciling the world to himself in Christ, not counting people's sins against them. And he has committed to us the message of reconciliation. We are therefore Christ's ambassadors, as though God were making his appeal through us. We implore you on Christ's behalf: Be reconciled to God. (2 Corinthians 5:18-20)

No matter where you go on social media, you will have ample opportunity to represent your Christian faith. It is all at your fingertips touching your screens: The images you share, your reactions to others, the words you post—all influence countless people who may not know the true message of Christ and what it means to follow Jesus. **It's murky water out there when it comes to staying true to our faith, and I want to help you learn how to stick to your Christian principles every time you get online.**

I want to help you navigate the online world with diligence and wisdom, grounded in the essential biblical principles of the Christian faith. Your own experience in the online world will surely be challenging and often confusing, even dangerous, as you discover new voices, opinions, images, and behaviors that are different from your own Christian values. Your world will expand exponentially as you dive deeper into the online world of social media and spend more time surfing the web to find entertainment and information, and it's important you learn how to manage your screen time in a Christ-like way.

I have created this workbook to address the most important Christian principles you need to understand and apply to your online (and offline) life. These biblical values will help you build the foundation of your faith and learn about Jesus. This workbook will walk you through what it means to truly follow Jesus as we dive into Scripture and set some goals for how you can put to practice every principle discussed.

Each lesson will be focused on one Christian principle, including important insights and Scripture to address and apply in managing your activity in the online world. I have included memory verses, worksheets, and checklists you can use that will help you grow your faith and strengthen your identity in Christ, so you can remain faithful amidst the challenges you face online as a Christian.

The following is a list of the Christian principles we will address in the upcoming chapters:

1. Love

2. Grace

3. Humility

4. Compassion

5. Truth

6. Wisdom

7. Integrity

8. Faithfulness

You will face many challenges, and you might even struggle to make godly choices as you grow and develop these characteristics, but remember that God wants the very best for you, and although you might fail at times, His love for you *never fails*. Hold onto that truth, and believe that God is with you every step you take; He longs to have you draw close to Him in every circumstance.

I pray this guide is a helpful tool that nourishes your faith and equips you with the love, grace, humility, compassion, truth, wisdom, integrity, and faithfulness you need to follow Jesus.

As you go through this guide, open your heart and allow the Holy Spirit to speak to you through His Word and teach you the ways in which He wants you to go—and the ways in which He wants you to follow Jesus.

Christian Principle #1:
LOVE

Discussion

> And now these three remain: faith, hope and love. But the greatest of these is love.
> (1 Corinthians 13:13)

If there is one word that could describe the Christian message and reflect the gospel, it is *love*. Christian love is a radical love. This kind of love is not a worldly, conditional love, but rather, it is an extreme, limitless love that far exceeds any human love. Our Christian faith is based on a love that does not discriminate, for God sent Jesus to reconcile with *all* of His children. Christ's message of love has no bounds; we are to love others as He loves each one of us.

When we look deeper into this powerful principle, we can identify three clear aspects of love we are to demonstrate as Christians in this world. Each facet is connected to one another, and all of them instruct us on how we are to love.

Let's take a look at each one in more detail.

1. God's Unfailing Love for His Creation

If we truly understand God's unfailing love for *all people*, then we will live our lives in obedience offering that same love to *all people*. Yes, that means that everyone we come in contact with is wholly loved by God, our Creator. We must demonstrate His love for others in everything we do, think, and say.

There is a wealth of Scripture that reflects God's great love for His creation—every single human soul created in His image! That means everyone—even those we see behaving poorly and saying hurtful words. Yes, even those who have broken laws, murdered innocent people, and acted atrociously. Our Heavenly Father loves them and longs to reach them, too.

> In the beginning, God created the heavens and the earth. (Genesis 1:1)

> So God created mankind in his own image, in the image of God he created them; male and female he created them. (Genesis 1:27)

From the beginning, God created heaven and earth to be a perfect residence for His beloved children. He wanted to have a deep, abiding relationship with every human being He created, but then sin entered the world, and the connection was broken.

God's greatest desire is to reach the hearts of all people who do not know of His love and restore His relationship with them.

It is with God's pure love that He offered His Son as a sacrifice in place of our sins, which separate us from God, so that He could re-establish an intimate relationship with us. Christ is God's great gift of love to mankind. God demonstrated His love to us through sacrificing His Son so that we could be reconciled with and redeemed by our Heavenly Father. We are called to honor God's love by loving Him with all our hearts, minds, and souls (Matthew 22:35-38).

2. Christ's Sacrificial Gift of Unconditional Love

Through God's sacrificial offering of His Son, Jesus Christ, we learn the ultimate demonstration of love through Christ's death on the cross. God longed to break the barrier of sin, so that He could unite once again with His children. And while we were still sinners, Christ, both blameless and pure of all sin, was beaten and crucified on our behalf so that the barrier of sin could be broken.

It is through Christ's resurrection that our relationship with God was restored. Our sin is forever redeemed through the saving grace of Christ. This love is what we, as Christians, must share with others: Christ's sacrificial, unconditional love. We must share His profound message that declares *all* people are worthy of having a relationship with God, the Father, through accepting the gift of salvation through Jesus Christ.

We all have unique personalities and character traits created by God, and we can share the love of Christ through our own individual life paths.

Jesus spent His entire ministry reaching those who lived in sin and many who did not *seem* worthy of God's love. He offered grace and the profound invitation to receive the gift of God's love with a relentless passion for the lost. Ultimately, we must come from this place of deep, abiding, Christ-like love in order to share it with the world and to reach those who do not fully understand the gift offered to everyone.

3. Loving One Another in the Same Way Christ Loves Us

Christ calls us to love one another as we would want to be loved. This "Golden Rule" is one of the two greatest commandments Jesus offers us instructing how to live a life of faith (Matthew 22:39). This is a very important instruction to follow when we communicate with others both offline and online. We must treat everyone the way we would want to be treated. Sadly, this is often not the case for many people. This may be your greatest challenge, as you encounter people you may not like both in the online world and offline world! We are called to care for our neighbor, serve those in need, and reach out to all people with the love of Christ. This not only applies to our brothers and sisters in Christ (fellow Christian believers); it is intended for *all* people we encounter.

Demonstrating Christ's love toward others can be the most significant way we demonstrate God's message to the world. There will be opportunities challenging us to love many people who seem unlovable, and there will be people in your life that you feel don't deserve the love of Christ! But you must remember that no one is perfect, and we *all* fall short of the glory of God—and yes, that includes you, too. We can be a great witness to the love of Christ when we love the unlovable. Many people don't understand this kind of love, and it's up to us to show them!

The most powerful growth in our faith can come from loving people the way Christ loves us.

It may be one of the hardest things you do in honoring Christ, but it will also draw you closer to and deepen your relationship with Jesus.

This type of sacrificial love is purely selfless, and we are all naturally very selfish people. Consider loving the unlovable as a sacrifice you offer up to God as your gift in return for His gracious love for you. For God's Word says:

> "A new command I give you: Love one another. As I have loved you, so you must love one another." (John 13:34)

God will work on transforming your heart to be more like Christ as you take those faithful steps toward loving others in this sacrificial and unconditional way. The more you love like He does, the closer you will feel to Him. And really, there's nothing better than that!

Scripture Reading and Instruction

Read through the Scripture listed in the following pages about LOVE: God's love, Christ's love, and how we are called to love one another.

As you read the Bible's instruction on this Christian principle, think through the questions below to get a better understanding of God's Word. Then pick one favorite verse to complete this worksheet.

1. Use your own words to describe what this verse says.

_____

_____

_____

_____

2. What does this verse mean to you?

_____

_____

_____

_____

3. What does this verse teach you?

_____

_____

_____

_____

Biblical Examples of God's Love

Give thanks to the LORD, for he is good.
His love endures forever. (Psalm 136:1)

***

But God demonstrates his own love for us in this: While we were still sinners, Christ died for us. (Romans 5:8)

***

See what great love the Father has lavished on us, that we should be called children of God! And that is what we are! The reason the world does not know us is that it did not know him. (1 John 3:1)

***

Know therefore that the LORD your God is God; he is the faithful God, keeping his covenant of love to a thousand generations of those who love him and keep his commandments. (Deuteronomy 7:9)

***

The Lord appeared to us in the past, saying:
"I have loved you with an everlasting love;
I have drawn you with unfailing kindness." (Jeremiah 31:3)

Biblical Examples of Christ's Love

"As the Father has loved me, so have I loved you. Now remain in my love." (John 15:9)

***

"Just as the Son of Man did not come to be served, but to serve, and to give his life as a ransom for many." (Matthew 20:28)

***

Now the tax collectors and sinners were all gathering around to hear Jesus. But the Pharisees and the teachers of the law muttered, "This man welcomes sinners and eats with them."

Then Jesus told them this parable: "Suppose one of you has a hundred sheep and loses one of them. Doesn't he leave the ninety-nine in the open country and go after the lost sheep until he finds it? And when he finds it, he joyfully puts it on his shoulders and goes home. Then he calls his friends and neighbors together and says, 'Rejoice with me; I have found my lost sheep.' I tell you that in the same way there will be more rejoicing in heaven over one sinner who repents than over ninety-nine righteous persons who do not need to repent."
(Luke 15:1-7)

***

…so that Christ may dwell in your hearts through faith. And I pray that you, being rooted and established in love, may have power, together with all the Lord's holy people, to grasp how wide and long and high and deep is the love of Christ, and to know this love that surpasses knowledge—that you may be filled to the measure of all the fullness of God. (Ephesians 3:17-19)

***

…and walk in the way of love, just as Christ loved us and gave himself up for us as a fragrant offering and sacrifice to God. (Ephesians 5:2)

Biblical Instruction to Love One Another

We love because he first loved us. (1 John 4:19)

***

"Do not seek revenge or bear a grudge against anyone among your people, but love your neighbor as yourself. I am the Lord." (Leviticus 19:18)

***

Be devoted to one another in love. Honor one another above yourselves. (Romans 12:10)

***

And this is his command: to believe in the name of his Son, Jesus Christ, and to love one another as he commanded us. (1 John 3:23)

***

This is how we know what love is: Jesus Christ laid down his life for us. And we ought to lay down our lives for our brothers and sisters. (1 John 3:16)

Memory Verses

Copy or tear out the following Bible verses for LOVE. Place them somewhere where you can see them every day. Memorize each verse so that God's Word is planted firmly in your heart.

Dear friends,
let us love one another,
for love comes from God.
Everyone who loves has been
born of God and knows
God.

1 John 4:7 NIV

But God demonstrates his own love for us in this: While we were still sinners, Christ died for us.

Romans 5:8 NIV

"A new command I give you: Love one another. As I have loved you, so you must love one another. By this everyone will know that you are my disciples, if you love one another."

John 13:34-35 NIV

Goals and Challenges

1. Identify two general goals you can actively apply online to demonstrate Christian LOVE.

> **GOAL:** I am going to work on loving others the way Christ loves me.

GOAL #1:

_____

GOAL #2:

_____

2. What are the challenges you face in having a Christ-like heart of LOVE online? Identify two specific areas of difficulty and how you will apply this principle of LOVE.

> **CHALLENGE:** I don't really share anything about God's love on social media, but I know I should.

> **APPLY LOVE BY:** I'm going to find more Christian posts or pictures that show God's love and Christ's saving gift of grace and then share them on social media.

CHALLENGE #1:

_____

APPLY LOVE BY:

_____

CHALLENGE #2:

_____

APPLY LOVE BY:

_____

Talking Tips

Find a trusted Christian mentor to discuss the answers to the following questions about LOVE with you:

❖ What are some ways you have reflected God's love with other people in your life, both online and offline?

_____

_____

❖ Are there people in your life whom you struggle to love like Jesus? Name them, and share why.

_____

_____

❖ Are there people in your life who demonstrate this principle of love really well? Who are they, and what do they do that you can try to emulate?

_____

_____

❖ What keeps you from sharing God's love online? Are you embarrassed or afraid of how it will be received? Or do you simply forget? Are there other reasons you may not share God's love with others?

_____

_____

❖ Do you share the Good News about Christ's sacrificial and redeeming love when you interact online? If so, how do you do this, and what do you say? If not, how could you do this?

_____

_____

Your Personal Checklist

Think through these questions to help you navigate the online world with a Christ-like heart of LOVE:

- ✓ Have I prayed about having a Christ-like heart of love before sharing anything online?

- ✓ Does how I engage online reflect God's love for *all* people?

- ✓ Do I share the unconditional love of Christ with others in my life?

- ✓ Am I obeying Christ's instruction to love one another as I would want to be loved?

- ✓ Am I loving others the way Christ loves me?

- ✓ Am I excluding anyone of feeling loved?

- ✓ Does my social media account reflect loving thoughts, actions, and words?

- ✓ Am I really loving my enemies with how I respond to the unlovable online?

- ✓ Am I demonstrating Christian love with non-Christian people?

- ✓ Are there people in my life I need to make more of an effort to love?

Prayer

Dear God,
I want to understand how deep Your love is for me and every person You created. Help me love others the way Jesus loves me, even those I struggle to love most. Show me the people You want me to tell about Your love, and give me the courage to share it with them.
In Jesus's name, I pray, Amen.

Christian Principle #2:
GRACE

Discussion

> For the grace of God has appeared that offers salvation to all people. (Titus 2:11)

Because humankind is separated from God through sin, God sent Jesus Christ to be the ultimate and perfect sacrifice for our sins so that He could re-establish a relationship with us. Through Christ's death and resurrection, He paid the price for all our sins. When we believe that Jesus is our personal Savior by accepting Him into our hearts and lives, we are given the extraordinary gift of God's grace. In accepting this free gift from God, we are fully reconciled with our Creator and our sins are forgiven. Our relationship with God is completely restored, and we have been given life eternal through His Son, Jesus Christ. There is nothing you can do to *earn* forgiveness of your sins; you must only make this one faithful, life-changing choice.

> For God so loved the world that he gave his one and only Son, that whoever believes in him shall not perish but have eternal life. (John 3:16)

> For it is by grace you have been saved, through faith—and this not from yourselves, it is the gift of God—not by works, so that no one can boast. (Ephesians 2:8–9)

As we have accepted Christ's gift of salvation, we, too, must offer others that same invitation we have received.

We, as Christians, can't decide *who can* be saved and *who can't*. Remember, we *all* fall short of the glory of God, and it is not our place to judge others unless we want to be judged ourselves. Christ died for each one of us, and He calls us to reach out to *all* people with the good news of salvation through Jesus Christ.

Jesus spent most of His ministry serving people who needed grace most. The religious leaders of the time were angry with Him for doing this, and yet Jesus came into the world to reach the people who were most in need of salvation.

> On hearing this, Jesus said to them, "It is not the healthy who need a doctor, but the sick. I have not come to call the righteous, but sinners." (Mark 2:17)

As Christians, we are called to demonstrate this extraordinary grace we are given and to forgive others as Christ forgives us. This might be the hardest part of being a Christian!

We are to extend the *same grace* Christ gives us despite our feelings, hurts, or desire to retaliate. When we choose to forgive, we are surrendering our pain—and those who have sinned against us—in prayer as we give it all to God and trust in His power to restore our hearts.

This act of obedience is often very difficult. It does not mean that we accept the offense, and it certainly does not mean that we don't take action to remedy the conflict. This is *heart* work that happens inside us through prayer, so that we honor the gift of grace we have been given. We ultimately grow closer to Jesus as we experience our own small sacrificial offering for Him. What's really amazing is how we will grow closer to Christ *each time* we offer forgiveness in His name and draw all our strength from the unconditional, merciful love of Jesus. These hard decisions to forgive others can ultimately transform our hearts and grow our faith as we become more intimate in our relationship with Jesus. We cannot do this hard "heart work" without the strength and power of Christ!

Forgiving others never means you allow negative actions to harm you or anyone else. You can still intervene to protect yourself and certainly not allow anyone to harm you in any way. God does not want you to get hurt while loving others, but it will happen because we are sinful and make mistakes. It's important to take wise steps toward resolving conflict with the people in your life who cause you pain. You can bring to light any wrongdoings you witness and be proactive in stopping destructive behavior you might see online through a well-thought-out intervention. As a Christian, you are responsible for your own response and actions in how you handle such situations. You need to remember that you are expected to demonstrate grace through everything you do.

Always pause and pray for God's guidance before you post any response to bad behavior you see online.

No matter where you go online, you will be exposed to a wide range of negative interactions, inappropriate behaviors, and even unlawful activity. Unfortunately, you might even encounter your own faithful friends falling far from the gracious heart of Christ in how they interact with others, too.

If you are struggling with anything you see on social media and don't know what to do, please reach out to a trusted mentor or your parents for guidance. If you witness any behavior that is illegal or dangerous, you must tell an adult or contact the authorities.

Other things you see online may present you with opportunities to intervene and address negative behaviors with the biblical balance of grace and truth. If you observe another person sharing hurtful, dishonest, inappropriate, or hateful posts anywhere online, here are four suggestions as to how you can respond:

1. First and foremost, you must pray.

Pray for God to guide you in how to honor Him in your response and for His guidance in this situation. Also pray for the person who is acting negatively, for God calls us to pray for our enemies. (I know it's hard, but I promise God will soften your heart through this prayer!)

2. If you are comfortable addressing that person directly, you can follow this guideline:

> "If your brother or sister sins, go and point out their fault, just between the two of you. If they listen to you, you have won them over. But if they will not listen, take one or two others along, so that 'every matter may be established by the testimony of two or three witnesses.' If they still refuse to listen, tell it to the church; and if they refuse to listen even to the church, treat them as you would a pagan or a tax collector." (Matthew 18:15-17)

The outcome can be productive if the other person is willing to receive the feedback. It is up to you to determine if this approach would be effective and if you should approach the offender alone or with the support of another person by your side. You might feel more comfortable first talking about the issue with a godly mentor or your parents to receive guidance.

Having strong support during times of conflict is so important.

If the person refuses to accept responsibility for their actions, then depending on the offense, you will need to tell an adult (parent, teacher, or any authority figure you trust) who can intervene instead. Once you report the behavior to a trusted adult, completely stop engaging with that person. Eliminate that person from your social media feeds, and resist any interaction with them. Continue to prayerfully surrender the situation and the person over to God; it is in His hands now, and it's now the adult's responsibility and not yours.

3. Another way to respond to negative, untruthful, and hurtful posts/pictures online is to disagree with the opinion using concise facts or gracious words addressing the post/picture.

What's most important is that as Christians we do not respond with the same disrespect, hate, and hurtful stance. A response to negative slander must be carefully thought out and controlled. If we interact with negative people in the same way they interact with us, we are perpetuating the very same hatred, hurt, and rage. Instead, we can respond with the truth and stick to the facts, while omitting any additional offensive language. If someone shares an opinion that is hurtful or disrespectful, you can respond with why you disagree, but do it with grace and not anger.

4. The last option in responding to inappropriate, unkind, and hurtful posts and pictures online is to remain silent.

In doing this, we can send a clear message that we do not support the person or the message this person is sending. If we don't feed the post with attention, we can inadvertently devalue that message by not responding or intervening. Sometimes ignoring people who seem to be fueled by offending or hurting others can be our greatest weapon. If the person is demeaning or disrespecting another person, we can instead approach the victim with support and loving attention, to further dismantle and disregard the offense of the bully.

As with each of these options, it is important that you pray for discernment (godly direction) and for the offender in addition to the victim.

Prayer is where we will seek the wisdom to make these significant choices and find the grace to forgive.

It's also important that you find supportive counsel from a trusted Christian adult when you are faced with hard decisions about what to do with anything negative that you see online.

Scripture Reading and Instruction

Read through the Scripture listed in the following pages about GRACE.

As you read the Bible's instruction on this Christian principle, think through the questions below to get a better understanding of God's Word. Then pick one favorite verse to complete this worksheet.

1. Use your own words to describe what this verse says.

_____

_____

_____

_____

2. What does this verse mean to you?

_____

_____

_____

_____

3. What does this verse teach you?

_____

_____

_____

_____

Biblical Instruction on Grace

"But to you who are listening I say: Love your enemies, do good to those who hate you, bless those who curse you, pray for those who mistreat you. If someone slaps you on one cheek, turn to them the other also. If someone takes your coat, do not withhold your shirt from them. Give to everyone who asks you, and if anyone takes what belongs to you, do not demand it back. Do to others as you would have them do to you." (Luke 6:27-31)

***

"Do not judge, and you will not be judged. Do not condemn, and you will not be condemned. Forgive, and you will be forgiven. Give, and it will be given to you. A good measure, pressed down, shaken together and running over, will be poured into your lap. For with the measure you use, it will be measured to you." (Luke 6:37-38)

***

"Why do you look at the speck of sawdust in your brother's eye and pay no attention to the plank in your own eye? How can you say to your brother, 'Brother, let me take the speck out of your eye,' when you yourself fail to see the plank in your own eye? You hypocrite, first take the plank out of your eye, and then you will see clearly to remove the speck from your brother's eye." (Luke 6:41-42)

***

Then Peter came to Jesus and asked, "Lord, how many times shall I forgive my brother or sister who sins against me? Up to seven times?"

Jesus answered, "I tell you, not seven times, but seventy-seven times." (Matthew 18:21-22)

***

Now this is our boast: Our conscience testifies that we have conducted ourselves in the world, and especially in our relations with you, with integrity and godly sincerity. We have done so, relying not on worldly wisdom but on God's grace. (2 Corinthians 1:12)

***

Therefore, as God's chosen people, holy and dearly loved, clothe yourselves with compassion, kindness, humility, gentleness and patience. Bear with each other and forgive one another if any of you has a grievance against someone. Forgive as the Lord forgave you. (Colossians 3:12-13)

***

Let your conversation be always full of grace, seasoned with salt, so that you may know how to answer everyone. (Colossians 4:6)

***

But the wisdom that comes from heaven is first of all pure; then peace-loving, considerate, submissive, full of mercy and good fruit, impartial and sincere. (James 3:17)

Memory Verses

Copy or tear out the following Bible verses for GRACE. Place them somewhere where you can see them every day. Memorize each verse so that God's Word is planted firmly in your heart.

You then,
my son,
be strong in the grace
that is in
Christ Jesus.

2 Timothy 2:1 NIV

For it is by grace
you have been saved,
through faith-
and this is not
from yourselves,
it is the gift of God-

Ephesians 2:8 NIV

Goals and Challenges

1. Identify two general goals you can actively apply online to demonstrate Christian GRACE.

GOAL: I'm going to try to forgive people who upset me because Christ forgave me.

GOAL #1:

_____

GOAL #2:

_____

2. What are the challenges you face in having a Christ-like heart of GRACE online? Identify two specific areas of difficulty and how you will apply this principle of GRACE.

CHALLENGE: I really struggle with this one person who is so rude online.

APPLY GRACE BY: I'm going to talk to my parents about it and figure out how I can stop it from happening. I'll also pray for this person and pray for guidance in how to deal with this.

CHALLENGE #1:

_____

APPLY GRACE BY:

_____

CHALLENGE #2:

_____

APPLY GRACE BY:

_____

Talking Tips

Find a trusted Christian mentor to discuss the answers to the following questions about GRACE with you:

❖ It can be really hard to offer forgiveness to those who hurt us. Can you share any struggles you have had with having a gracious heart toward others?

_____

_____

❖ Do you know anyone who practices the principle of grace really well? Can you give some examples of how they demonstrate Christ-like grace?

_____

_____

❖ Is there something online you have seen that needs to be resolved by using the biblical steps outlined in Matthew 18:15-17? If so, ask your mentor to help you create a strategy.

_____

_____

❖ Have you witnessed destructive or dangerous behavior online before? Have you or someone you know been harmed in any way? Let's discuss what appropriate interventions need to take place.

_____

_____

❖ To whom can you go for support and help if you have seen negative or illegal behavior online? Why is this person someone you trust?

_____

_____

Your Personal Checklist

Think through these questions to help you navigate the online world with a Christ-like heart of GRACE:

- ✓ Have I prayed about having a Christ-like heart of grace before posting or responding to others online?

- ✓ How can I offer my opinion with grace-filled words?

- ✓ Am I addressing hate with love, anger with peace, hurt with compassion?

- ✓ What is the most productive and grace-filled way I can respond to inappropriate pictures or posts?

- ✓ Do the posts and pictures I share reflect Christ's unconditional grace for all people?

- ✓ Do I need wise counsel from a trusted mentor before I respond to inappropriate behavior that I see online?

- ✓ Have I checked my own heart/actions for any wrongdoing? If I am to blame, am I taking responsibility and asking for forgiveness?

- ✓ Do I offer forgiveness to those who hurt or offend me?

- ✓ Have I offered support to any friends who have had negative interactions with others online?

- ✓ Do I need to contact an authority and report any illegal or dangerous behavior I have witnessed?

Prayer

Dear God,
Please help me grow in Your grace so I can draw from it to forgive others. I'm so grateful You forgive all my sins through Your Son's sacrifice on the cross. I want it to sink into my heart and feel the peace of knowing You love me no matter what mistakes I make.
In Jesus's name, I pray, Amen.

Christian Principle #3:
HUMILITY

Discussion

> Be completely humble and gentle; be patient, bearing with one another in love. (Ephesians 4:2)

Jesus demonstrated humility in everything He did and said, and He calls us all to do the same. Through His entire ministry, we see how Jesus came not to be served, but to serve. If we have a deep understanding of His teachings, we can clearly see how important humility is at the core of following Jesus.

> "For even the Son of Man did not come to be served, but to serve, and to give his life as a ransom for many." (Mark 10:45)

Jesus talked often about being humble and how pride and arrogance are unacceptable in the eyes of the Lord. He exemplified what it truly means to live a life of humility as He offered love to the unlovable and grace to the unforgivable. In His last meal with His disciples, He showed a remarkable demonstration of being a humble servant and commanded them to live this way as well:

> When he had finished washing their feet, he put on his clothes and returned to his place. "Do you understand what I have done for you?" he asked them. "You call me 'Teacher' and 'Lord,' and rightly so, for that is what I am. Now that I, your Lord and Teacher, have washed your feet, you also should wash one another's feet. I have set you an example that you should do as I have done for you." (John 13:12-15)

The Christian principle of humility is one of the greatest challenges to our character.

We humans are so prideful, aren't we? The Bible has several verses on pride and how it keeps us from having an intimate relationship with Christ. It takes humility to open our hearts and let go of our own control over our lives. It takes humility to serve others, to sacrifice our selfish desires, and to seek God's guidance.

When we live our lives according to Jesus's standards, we must always be mindful of our hearts and make sure we are growing in humility as Christians. But what does that actually look like? We have the heart of humility when we choose to do the following:

- Accept apologies

- Understand another person's perspective
- Acknowledge other people's victories, triumphs, and successes
- Offer our services, time, and help to others
- Love others where they are
- Forgive others for hurting us
- Not boast about our own achievements, opinions, or gifts
- Not be jealous of another person's success
- Not post words or pictures in order to gain attention
- Encourage others to feel confident in their talents, identity, and goals
- Sacrifice our own desires to meet the needs of others
- Not need to be right all the time
- Be patient with difficult people
- Bring peace to a conflict
- Be generous with our time and resources
- Think about others instead of ourselves
- Be considerate and kind, no matter how we feel
- Have a deep understanding that God deserves the credit and not us
- Be others-focused instead of self-centered

We don't realize how often pride is at the root of our choices, reactions, emotions, and attitudes. It's easy to base our opinions and perspective on our own understanding and experiences and not step outside ourselves to take on a godly view instead. We are quick to defend our ideas and beliefs against anyone who threatens them. We are also prone to make decisions from a deep sense of selfish ambition, self-protection, and a desire for affirmation. Our motivation often stems from our subconscious need to be safe, comfortable, and accepted.

We need to take a hard look at what motivates our actions and ask God to reveal where pride may be lurking.

It's important to note that acting in humility does not mean that we allow ourselves to be victims. There is a significant boundary God honors in giving us permission to set limits on our interactions with people who hurt us, threaten our well-being, or are dangerous in any way. We can serve, support, forgive, and sacrificially give of ourselves to others, but we also need to take care of our own health and well-being. We need to protect ourselves from harm. It's a delicate balance of being selfless and nourishing ourselves, too. God wants to fill us with sustenance to do His work with those who need to learn about Christ, but He doesn't want us to be drained or victimized in the process.

There are so many opportunities to practice this principle online through social media. Practicing self-control and being mindful of how you interact with people while being humble online can be difficult. Social media is where we want to celebrate our lives and post our accomplishments, hoping for a lot of praise in return. It's okay to want to share about your achievements or fun times with friends and also to want positive feedback! We all enjoy that! Just make sure you are doing so without boasting arrogantly or constantly focusing on yourself. Also, make sure you are supporting your friends when they, too, share special moments and post about themselves.

Scripture Reading and Instruction

Read through the Scripture listed in the following pages about HUMILITY.

As you read the Bible's instruction on this Christian principle, think through the questions below to get a better understanding of God's Word. Then pick one favorite verse to complete this worksheet.

1. Use your own words to describe what this verse says.

_____

_____

_____

_____

2. What does this verse mean to you?

_____

_____

_____

_____

3. What does this verse teach you?

_____

_____

_____

_____

Biblical Instruction on Humility

Sitting down, Jesus called the Twelve and said, "Anyone who wants to be first must be the very last, and the servant of all." (Mark 9:35)

***

"For even the Son of Man did not come to be served, but to serve, and to give his life as a ransom for many." (Mark 10:45)

***

Do nothing out of selfish ambition or vain conceit. Rather, in humility value others above yourselves. (Philippians 2:3)

***

When pride comes, then comes disgrace, but with humility comes wisdom. (Proverbs 11:2)

***

Live in harmony with one another. Do not be proud, but be willing to associate with people of low position. Do not be conceited. (Romans 12:16)

***

Your beauty should not come from outward adornment, such as elaborate hairstyles and the wearing of gold jewelry or fine clothes. Rather, it should be that of your inner self, the unfading beauty of a gentle and quiet spirit, which is of great worth in God's sight. (1 Peter 3:3-4)

***

But he gives us more grace. That is why Scripture says: "God opposes the proud but shows favor to the humble." (James 4:6)

Memory Verses

Copy or tear out the following Bible verses for HUMILITY. Place them somewhere where you can see them every day. Memorize each verse so that God's Word is planted firmly in your heart.

Be completely humble
and gentle; be patient,
bearing with one another
in love.

Ephesians 4:2 NIV

Humble yourselves before the Lord, and he will lift you up.

James 4:10 NIV

Goals and Challenges

1. Identify two general goals you can actively apply online to demonstrate Christian HUMILITY.

> **GOAL:** I will try to spend less time focusing on me and more time supporting my friends online.

GOAL #1:

GOAL #2:

---

2. What are the challenges you face in having a Christ-like heart of HUMILITY online? Identify two specific areas of difficulty and how you will apply this principle of HUMILITY.

> **CHALLENGE:** I focus too much on how many likes I get on my pictures.
>
> **APPLY HUMILITY BY:** I'm going to focus more on how God wants me to interact online and less about my own motives.

CHALLENGE #1:

APPLY HUMILITY BY:

CHALLENGE #2:

APPLY HUMILITY BY:

Talking Tips

Find a trusted Christian mentor to discuss the answers to the following questions about HUMILITY with you:

❖ What are some challenges you experience when it comes to your own pride?

_____

_____

❖ Can you share ways you have been able to practice humility successfully, either with your friends or family or in your activity online?

_____

_____

❖ Do you know people in your life who are great examples of being humble and sacrificial and not prideful or selfish? In what ways have they made an impact on you?

_____

_____

❖ Do you encounter many prideful people and posts online? How do you respond?

_____

_____

❖ What are some new ways in which you can be more intentional about practicing humility on social media?

_____

_____

Your Personal Checklist

Think through these questions to help you navigate the online world with a Christ-like heart of HUMILITY:

- ✓ Have I prayed about having a Christ-like heart of humility before posting or responding to others online?

- ✓ Is what I'm about to post boastful or selfish in any way?

- ✓ Am I responding to others with a humble heart or a prideful heart?

- ✓ Do I want to be right more than I want to understand other people's opinions?

- ✓ Am I considering the feelings of others?

- ✓ Am I supporting my friends with love and encouragement?

- ✓ Am I putting God's truth before my own opinion?

- ✓ Am I serving my own needs or serving the needs of others?

- ✓ Am I giving credit (to God) where credit is due?

- ✓ Am I focusing too much on how many likes I get when I share posts and pictures on social media?

Prayer

Dear God,
Please open my eyes to my selfish ways so I can grow to be less prideful in everything I do and say. Help me stretch beyond myself to see the needs of others and to understand other people's points of view. Show me ways I can be more sacrificial and serving.
In Jesus's name, I pray, Amen.

Christian Principle #4:
COMPASSION

Discussion

> The LORD is gracious and righteous;
> our God is full of compassion. (Psalm 116:5)

All of these Christian principles are connected in many ways. Once we have the love of Christ in our hearts, we can be filled with His enduring grace and a heart of humility. Those three characteristics naturally give way to compassion. The second greatest commandment, referred to as the "Golden Rule," is loving one another, and an important piece to this love is demonstrated through the heart of compassion.

> "So in everything, do to others what you would have them do to you, for this sums up the Law and the Prophets." (Matthew 7:12)

Compassion is birthed from having a loving, gracious, and humble heart.

The online world offers us ample opportunity to view the world and the people in it. Their stories, circumstances, and life events are often shared through social media. As we learn about the struggles and challenges that people face, we can respond with compassion by sharing encouraging words, offering help, and praying for them. We are called to love one another in this way.

As Christians, we must follow Jesus by tuning in and tending to the needs of others. We need to be aware of other people in our lives. All the "status" updates present us with even more people experiencing a struggle, hardship, or crisis. You might be scrolling through your social media feeds quickly, not even thinking about being compassionate if you see someone hurting, but it's a perspective we must take on. Remember to keep an eye out for anyone who might be struggling in some way, and take the time to respond with compassion. Doing this is so pleasing to God and truly feels good, too!

We may not be able to change their situation or circumstance, but Christ deploys us out into the world to care for others in any realistic way that we can. This may mean simply offering prayer, providing a service, or sharing encouraging words and support. It's up to each one of us to prayerfully decide where God wants us to be in a person's life and act accordingly.

There are many examples of having a Christ-like heart of compassion in the Bible, for Jesus's ministry was clearly defined by His love and deep concern for all.

Our Christian walk involves having a heart for others and caring deeply for all people. True compassion is when a person has empathy for one who is suffering and a passionate desire to help that person in their plight. Jesus is our best role model. He showed His profound compassion throughout His ministry of healing the sick, reaching out to the lost, and ministering to the multitudes with a generous outpouring of service. He ultimately demonstrated the most compassionate act of all—dying on the cross to save humanity from our sin. We can learn so much about compassion from Jesus's life on earth.

> When Jesus landed and saw a large crowd, he had compassion on them and healed their sick. (Matthew 14:14)

> When the Lord saw her, his heart went out to her and he said, "Don't cry." (Luke 7:13)

In establishing your identity in Christ, it's important that you develop a heart for others and learn how to put love into action.

Being aware of the needs of others is an ongoing challenge no matter how old you are. It's a natural impulse to think of our own situations and feelings, and tend to our own needs, but Christ calls us to serve and love one another, always stretching our hands to reach those who need our care, support, and help.

Scripture Reading and Instruction

Read through the Scripture listed in the following pages about COMPASSION.

As you read the Bible's instruction on this Christian principle, think through the questions below to get a better understanding of God's Word. Then pick one favorite verse to complete this worksheet.

1. Use your own words to describe what this verse says.

_____

_____

_____

_____

2. What does this verse mean to you?

_____

_____

_____

_____

3. What does this verse teach you?

_____

_____

_____

_____

Biblical Instruction on Compassion

The Parable of the Good Samaritan

On one occasion an expert in the law stood up to test Jesus. "Teacher," he asked, "what must I do to inherit eternal life?"

"What is written in the Law?" he replied. "How do you read it?"

He answered, "'Love the Lord your God with all your heart and with all your soul and with all your strength and with all your mind'; and, 'Love your neighbor as yourself.'"

"You have answered correctly," Jesus replied. "Do this and you will live."

But he wanted to justify himself, so he asked Jesus, "And who is my neighbor?"

In reply Jesus said: "A man was going down from Jerusalem to Jericho, when he was attacked by robbers. They stripped him of his clothes, beat him and went away, leaving him half dead. A priest happened to be going down the same road, and when he saw the man, he passed by on the other side. So too, a Levite, when he came to the place and saw him, passed by on the other side. But a Samaritan, as he traveled, came where the man was; and when he saw him, he took pity on him. He went to him and bandaged his wounds, pouring on oil and wine. Then he put the man on his own donkey, brought him to an inn and took care of him. The next day he took out two denarii and gave them to the innkeeper. 'Look after him,' he said, 'and when I return, I will reimburse you for any extra expense you may have.'

"Which of these three do you think was a neighbor to the man who fell into the hands of robbers?"

The expert in the law replied, "The one who had mercy on him."

Jesus told him, "Go and do likewise." (Luke 10:25-37)

***

Suppose a brother or a sister is without clothes and daily food. If one of you says to them, "Go in peace; keep warm and well fed," but does nothing about their physical needs, what good is it? (James 2:15-16)

***

Praise be to the God and Father of our Lord Jesus Christ, the Father of compassion and the God of all comfort, who comforts us in all our troubles, so that we can comfort those in any trouble with the comfort we ourselves receive from God. (2 Corinthians 1:3-4)

***

Finally, all of you, be like-minded, be sympathetic, love one another, be compassionate and humble. (1 Peter 3:8)

***

Carry each other's burdens, and in this way you will fulfill the law of Christ. (Galatians 6:2)

***

"'For I was hungry and you gave me something to eat, I was thirsty and you gave me something to drink, I was a stranger and you invited me in, I needed clothes and you clothed me, I was sick and you looked after me, I was in prison and you came to visit me.'

"Then the righteous will answer him, 'Lord, when did we see you hungry and feed you, or thirsty and give you something to drink? When did we see you a stranger and invite you in, or needing clothes and clothe you? When did we see you sick or in prison and go to visit you?'

"The King will reply, 'Truly I tell you, whatever you did for one of the least of these brothers and sisters of mine, you did for me.'" (Matthew 25:35-40)

Memory Verses

Copy or tear out the following Bible verses for COMPASSION. Place them somewhere where you can see them every day. Memorize each verse so that God's Word is planted firmly in your heart.

Be kind and compassionate
to one another,
forgiving each other,
just as in Christ God
forgave you.

Ephesians 4:32 NIV

Therefore, as God's chosen people, holy and dearly loved, clothe yourselves with compassion, kindness, humility, gentleness and patience.

Colossians 3:12 NIV

Goals and Challenges

1. Identify two general goals you can actively apply online to demonstrate Christian COMPASSION.

> **GOAL:** I'm going to reach out more to people I see online who seem unhappy.

GOAL #1:

GOAL #2:

---

2. What are the challenges you face in having a Christ-like heart of COMPASSION online? Identify two specific areas of difficulty and how you will apply this principle of COMPASSION.

> **CHALLENGE:** I want to be more encouraging to a friend who is going through some hard times.
>
> **APPLY COMPASSION BY:** I'm going to message her the next time she posts something about her situation.

CHALLENGE #1:

APPLY COMPASSION BY:

CHALLENGE #2:

APPLY COMPASSION BY:

Talking Tips

Find a trusted Christian mentor to discuss the answers to the following questions about COMPASSION with you:

❖ Do you struggle to have compassion for certain people you know? Why do you think that is?

_____

_____

❖ What's the biggest challenge you face in being compassionate with others?

_____

_____

❖ Who in your life demonstrates this principle really well, and how?

_____

_____

❖ What are some examples of you demonstrating being compassionate with others in your life?

_____

_____

❖ How do you practice this principle online? What are some additional ways in which you can be more compassionate with others on social media?

_____

_____

Your Personal Checklist

Think through these questions to help you navigate the online world with a Christ-like heart of COMPASSION:

- ✓ Have I prayed about having a Christ-like heart of compassion before getting online?

- ✓ Am I considering the needs of others when I'm on social media?

- ✓ Am I responding to friends' difficult situations with concern and support?

- ✓ Am I being compassionate with people I don't even like?

- ✓ How can I serve people I see online who are suffering?

- ✓ Does what I'm about to share send a message of compassion?

- ✓ Am I having empathy for others when I interact online?

- ✓ Am I praying for the people who are experiencing hardship?

- ✓ Am I spending more time focused on me or other people when I'm on social media?

- ✓ Are there other ways in which I can demonstrate compassion online?

Prayer

Dear God,
Help me tune into people who are struggling, and teach me how to reach out and offer them help, encouragement, and prayer. Fill my heart with compassion for those in need, and show me how I can best serve people who are hurting.
In Jesus's name, I pray, Amen.

Christian Principle #5:
TRUTH

Discussion

> To the Jews who had believed him, Jesus said, "If you hold to my teaching, you are really my disciples. Then you will know the truth, and the truth will set you free." (John 8:31-32)

The principle of truth (and the importance of it) is found not only in the Ten Commandments (God's laws) but all over the Bible. Honesty is a very important value we must practice as Christians because God implores us not only to speak truth in everything that we do but also to understand that the Word of God *is* truth—truth we must always work hard to apply to our lives. Ultimately, Jesus declared that He is the way, the truth, and the life and that no one can come to God except through Him.

> Jesus answered, "I am the way and the truth and the life. No one comes to the Father except through me." (John 14:6)

That profound message is at the very core of our faith. What Jesus stands for, demonstrates, and calls us to do is not only to believe in His truth but also to live our lives according to *all* truth in God's Word, *The Holy Bible*.

We also need to be truthful in how we interact with others. When we are able to live our lives with a clear conscience of honesty, we are free from the heavy weight of lies that can create a barrier in our relationship with the Lord and of course with the people we deceive. When we are truthful, we can be trusted. When we are dishonest, we create distance, conflicts, and pain. If we follow Jesus, we must testify to the ultimate truth of salvation, but who will believe us if we have not been truthful? More importantly, if we aren't truthful, how will people trust our relationship with Jesus to be true?

Living a life of truth can be quite challenging in a world that is littered with dishonesty, especially when it comes to content posted online. The value placed on truth has eroded in today's world, as it is nearly impossible to know what is and isn't true as we filter through "fake news" and false claims every day. We must be careful about who and what we trust. It is impossible to trust what we see or hear these days without fact-checking every claim. Unfortunately, we live in times when lying is the norm and truth is rare. This is in our culture now more than ever; the online world is filled with deceit.

This type of dishonest culture can slowly seep into our own perspective with lies that misguide us in our thinking, actions, and responses.

We can lose sight of what is real, just, and true when we are surrounded by fake news and images every day. We may even dismantle our own truths as we are tempted to conform to what others are doing, thinking, or saying. This can leave us vulnerable and can weaken our faith. Make sure you are always on guard in understanding what is true and what is not, so you don't fall victim to schemes or people who have selfish motives.

The greatest threat to our faith is from other Christians who distort God's Word with confusing and deceptive messages. There are many "false teachers" out there who can mislead you with inaccurate "biblical truths." Please don't believe everything you read and hear, and don't trust that all Christians are trust-*worthy* or that their messages are true.

If you are a newer Christian, you are especially susceptible to believing what you read online because you may not know a lot of Scripture; you may not yet understand what is biblically true. It can be very dangerous to your Christian walk if you automatically believe everything you see, so please ask a trusted Christian mentor when you see something about your faith that you don't understand.

The Bible is our resource for truth. We must continue to study Scripture with a trusted Christian leader to lay a firm foundation for our faith, so we are capable of knowing the difference between what is true and what is not.

It's easy to develop a negative view of ourselves as we scroll through social media filled with everyone's highlight reel of exciting experiences and achievements along with perfectly filtered pictures. It's also very easy to look to other people's social media feed as a basis to measure our own self-worth. We are constantly comparing ourselves to others, and often this can be discouraging and feel defeating. Social media is full of images and messages that can make anyone feel as if they don't measure up. But the truth is, people only share the very best parts of their lives and rarely reveal any of their pain or weaknesses with the online world. I'm guessing you do the same. Just remember, what you see on social media is not the entire picture of anyone's life. We must be aware that everyone has struggles and no one is perfect!

There is great pressure out there to fit in, to look good, and to be accepted and liked in the growing culture of deception and manipulation.

Most importantly, never forget: God created us differently, giving each of us our own gifts, strengths, personality traits, and life circumstances that are designed to fulfill His purpose for our lives.

There's simply no way to compare ourselves to others when God designed each one of us according to how He wants us to live. Each person is made with unique, incomparable qualities. No two people are alike. So, embrace who *you* are and use *your* God-given gifts without worrying about someone else's.

> For you created my inmost being;
> you knit me together in my mother's womb.
> I praise you because I am fearfully and wonderfully made;
> your works are wonderful,
> I know that full well. (Psalm 139:13-14)

Scripture Reading and Instruction

Read through the Scripture listed in the following pages about TRUTH.

As you read the Bible's instruction on this Christian principle, think through the questions below to get a better understanding of God's Word. Then pick one favorite verse to complete this worksheet.

1. Use your own words to describe what this verse says.

_____

_____

_____

_____

2. What does this verse mean to you?

_____

_____

_____

_____

3. What does this verse teach you?

_____

_____

_____

_____

Biblical Instruction on Truth

To the Jews who had believed him, Jesus said, "If you hold to my teaching, you are really my disciples. Then you will know the truth, and the truth will set you free." (John 8:31-32)

***

Do your best to present yourself to God as one approved, a worker who does not need to be ashamed and who correctly handles the word of truth. (2 Timothy 2:15)

***

Therefore, each of you must put off falsehood and speak truthfully to your neighbor, for we are all members of one body. (Ephesians 4:25)

***

"…and many false prophets will appear and deceive many people." (Matthew 24:11)

***

In the presence of God and of Christ Jesus, who will judge the living and the dead, and in view of his appearing and his kingdom, I give you this charge: Preach the word; be prepared in season and out of season; correct, rebuke and encourage—with great patience and careful instruction. For the time will come when people will not put up with sound doctrine. Instead, to suit their own desires, they will gather around them a great number of teachers to say what their itching ears want to hear. They will turn their ears away from the truth and turn aside to myths. But you, keep your head in all situations, endure hardship, do the work of an evangelist, discharge all the duties of your ministry. (2 Timothy 4:1-5)

***

If we claim to have fellowship with him and yet walk in the darkness, we lie and do not live out the truth. (1 John 1:6)

***

"You shall not give false testimony against your neighbor." (Exodus 20:16)

***

No one who practices deceit
will dwell in my house;
no one who speaks falsely
will stand in my presence. (Psalm 101:7)

Memory Verses

Copy or tear out the following Bible verses for TRUTH. Place them somewhere where you can see them every day. Memorize each verse so that God's Word is planted firmly in your heart.

Dear children,
let us not love
with words or speech
but with actions
and in truth.

1 John 3:18 NIV

"God is spirit,
and his worshipers
must worship in the Spirit
and in truth."

John 4:24 NIV

Goals and Challenges

1. Identify two general goals you can actively apply online to demonstrate Christian TRUTH.

> **GOAL:** I'm not going to believe everything I read and see online.

GOAL #1:

_____

GOAL #2:

_____

2. What are the challenges you face in having a Christ-like heart of TRUTH online? Identify two specific areas of difficulty and how you will apply this principle of TRUTH.

> **CHALLENGE:** I often feel jealous and compare myself to others on social media.

> **APPLY TRUTH BY:** I must remember that I was created for a purpose and find my worth in Christ, not man.

CHALLENGE #1:

_____

APPLY TRUTH BY:

_____

CHALLENGE #2:

_____

APPLY TRUTH BY:

_____

Talking Tips

Find a trusted Christian mentor to discuss the answers to the following questions about TRUTH with you:

❖ What are some of the messages you see online that you know for sure aren't true? Explain.

_____

_____

❖ Who do you compare yourself to, and how does it make you feel? How do you define success? How do you think God defines success?

_____

_____

❖ Which sites do you follow online that you trust? Which sites should you steer away from?

_____

_____

❖ Are there certain things you see online about the Christian faith that confuse you? If so, what are they, and who can you talk to about them?

_____

_____

❖ Who can you talk to if you see questionable information online? What resources can you use to fact-check any information you find on the internet?

_____

_____

Your Personal Checklist

Think through these questions to help you navigate the online world with a Christ-like heart of TRUTH:

- ✓ Have I prayed for God to reveal truth to me?

- ✓ Do I measure my worth by social media likes or by how God sees me?

- ✓ Do I need to investigate certain claims before I believe them?

- ✓ Is every Christian message I see biblically true?

- ✓ Is everything I share online entirely true?

- ✓ Am I believing statements online without fact-checking?

- ✓ If I see something that is confusing, do I ask someone I trust to get clarity?

- ✓ Am I aware that not all pictures are portrayed accurately?

- ✓ Do I always consider the source from where I read information?

- ✓ Am I being mindful in deciding who I trust online?

Prayer

Dear God,
Help me understand Your Word so I know what is and isn't true about my faith. Reveal all the falsehoods I see online so I'm not misled. Please guide me in all my decisions and show me the sites and people I can trust. May I honor both being truthful and Your Truth. In Jesus's name, I pray, Amen.

Christian Principle #6:
WISDOM

Discussion

> But the wisdom that comes from heaven is first of all pure; then peace-loving, considerate, submissive, full of mercy and good fruit, impartial and sincere. (James 3:17)

Wisdom comes from understanding God's truth and applying Scripture to our values, views, actions, and ongoing decisions in our daily walk of faith. As we grow as Christians, firmly planting our footing in biblical truth, we are able to walk in the knowledge God provides through His Word. The Bible can be our most important guide for how we do life.

> Your word is a lamp for my feet,
> a light on my path. (Psalm 119:105)

As we grow in our faith, we allow the Holy Spirit to minister to our minds and hearts through the power of God's Word. We must have wisdom to navigate our path and make godly decisions based on truth. The more we grow in wisdom, the stronger we will become in our faith and the more equipped we will be in understanding how God wants us to live.

Christian wisdom should guide us in every aspect of our lives.

When our relationship with Jesus becomes more intimate and we seek Him in all that we do, we begin to develop godly discernment. Discernment means carefully applying biblical instruction to decisions we make every day. Christians must constantly make careful choices that honor God in every area of our lives (including what we do online!). If we don't have wisdom to discern right from wrong, we become vulnerable to straying from our faith.

Wisdom comes with age and experience. You may not have a firm grasp on all Scripture just yet in your walk with the Lord, so it's important you find trusted mentors to disciple you and help you understand the Bible. The more you study God's Word, the deeper your faith will grow. As you mature in a better understanding of what it means to live your life anchored in Christ, you will gain wisdom.

The more life you experience as a Christian, the more you will learn to apply God's Word to all your decisions and the wiser you will become. Knowing what is right and wrong can be confusing for any of us! Prayer is essential in developing discernment, and

Christian fellowship is the best way to receive support in making godly decisions rooted in your faith. Surround yourself with other believers who can help you grow in wisdom.

You will encounter many different views and voices online that do not align with God's Word. It's so important that you don't believe everything you see but instead seek the truth in Scripture or ask a trusted mentor.

> Then we will no longer be infants, tossed back and forth by the waves, and blown here and there by every wind of teaching and by the cunning and craftiness of people in their deceitful scheming. (Ephesians 4:14)

Anytime you are surfing the web or scrolling through social media, use biblical discernment in choosing what you see and what you share. Remember to carefully think through everything you see online in order to distinguish right from wrong and truth from deception.

Making wise decisions will help you stay safe and stick to your Christian principles.

Scripture Reading and Instruction

Read through the Scripture listed in the following pages about WISDOM.

As you read the Bible's instruction on this Christian principle, think through the questions below to get a better understanding of God's Word. Then pick one favorite verse to complete this worksheet.

1. Use your own words to describe what this verse says.

_____

_____

_____

_____

2. What does this verse mean to you?

_____

_____

_____

_____

3. What does this verse teach you?

_____

_____

_____

_____

Biblical Instruction on Wisdom

"Therefore, everyone who hears these words of mine and puts them into practice is like a wise man who built his house on the rock. The rain came down, the streams rose, and the winds blew and beat against that house; yet it did not fall, because it had its foundation on the rock." (Matthew 7:24-25)

***

If any of you lacks wisdom, you should ask God, who gives generously to all without finding fault, and it will be given to you. But when you ask, you must believe and not doubt, because the one who doubts is like a wave of the sea, blown and tossed by the wind. That person should not expect to receive anything from the Lord. Such a person is double-minded and unstable in all they do. (James 1:5-8)

***

The fear of the LORD is the beginning of wisdom;
all who follow his precepts have good understanding.
To him belongs eternal praise. (Psalm 111:10)

***

Those who are wise will shine like the brightness of the heavens, and those who lead many to righteousness, like the stars for ever and ever. (Daniel 12:3)

***

I keep asking that the God of our Lord Jesus Christ, the glorious Father, may give you the Spirit of wisdom and revelation, so that you may know him better. (Ephesians 1:17)

***

Dear friends, do not believe every spirit, but test the spirits to see whether they are from God, because many false prophets have gone out into the world. (1 John 4:1)

***

My goal is that they may be encouraged in heart and united in love, so that they may have the full riches of complete understanding, in order that they may know the mystery of God, namely, Christ, in whom are hidden all the treasures of wisdom and knowledge. (Colossians 2:2-3)

Memory Verses

Copy or tear out the following Bible verses for WISDOM. Place them somewhere where you can see them every day. Memorize each verse so that God's Word is planted firmly in your heart.

Blessed are those who find wisdom, those who gain understanding.

Proverbs 3:13 NIV

Walk with the wise
and become wise,
for a companion of fools
suffers harm.

Proverbs 13:20 NIV

Goals and Challenges

1. Identify two general goals you can actively apply online to demonstrate Christian WISDOM.

>**GOAL:** I'm going to participate in the Bible study that my youth group is doing so I can learn more about the Bible.

GOAL #1:

_____

GOAL #2:

_____

2. What are the challenges you face in having a Christ-like heart of WISDOM online? Identify two specific areas of difficulty and how you will apply this principle of WISDOM.

>**CHALLENGE:** I don't always understand a lot of what Christians share on social media.

>**APPLY WISDOM BY:** I'm going to ask my youth pastor about things I see online so I can learn what is and isn't true about my faith.

CHALLENGE #1:

_____

APPLY WISDOM BY:

_____

CHALLENGE #2:

_____

APPLY WISDOM BY:

_____

Talking Tips

Find a trusted Christian mentor to discuss the answers to the following questions about WISDOM with you:

❖ Are there personal experiences or issues that you want to talk about and understand better, according to our faith? What are they?

_____

_____

❖ There's a lot going on online. What are some Christian topics you hear about or see online that concern or confuse you that you want to learn more about?

_____

_____

❖ Do you have a Christian mentor who is wise? Are you able to talk with that person regularly about your faith? If not, how might you connect with one?

_____

_____

❖ What are some ways in which you can confirm that what you see online is aligned with the Christian faith? Let's brainstorm some resources and contacts you can use to help you seek the truth.

_____

_____

❖ In order to grow in wisdom, you need to understand God's Word. What goals can you set for reading the Bible? What structure in your routine will help you to make those goals sustainable?

_____

_____

Your Personal Checklist

Think through these questions to help you navigate the online world with a Christ-like heart of WISDOM:

- ✓ Have I prayed for God to guide me in discernment (understanding right from wrong according to God's Word)?

- ✓ Does this viewpoint I am reading align with biblical truth?

- ✓ Have I searched Scripture related to this topic I'm questioning?

- ✓ Do I need to seek an authority figure in my faith to discern what's true and not true?

- ✓ Am I responding to people online the way God expects me to?

- ✓ Am I making wise decisions according to my faith as to where I go online?

- ✓ When I see something ungodly online, do I make the right choice in how I respond?

- ✓ Am I making wise choices in whom I follow and what I share online?

- ✓ What steps should I take to further investigate new topics I know little about?

- ✓ Am I applying what I learn in Scripture to what I see and share online?

Prayer

Dear God,
Help me make wise decisions about who I follow and where I go online. Guide me in my interactions with others, and teach me to discern right from wrong according to You. Show me how to follow Jesus in everything I do and say.
In Jesus's name, I pray, Amen.

Christian Principle #7:
INTEGRITY

Discussion

> Blessed are those whose ways are blameless,
> who walk according to the law of the Lord. (Psalm 119:1)

The principle of Christian integrity is a culmination of all the previous character traits discussed so far. If we commit to following Jesus, we will consequently grow in love, grace, humility, compassion, truth, and wisdom, and regularly live by all of these principles.

When we consistently behave according to our Christian principles, we are living a life of Christian integrity. Sadly, there isn't much evidence of this principle in the world—either on- or offline, so it's really important you choose your Christian role models carefully. Nobody is perfect, so always understand that even the strongest, most faithful Christian is flawed and will make mistakes. However, we can learn so much from people who truly demonstrate all the Christian principles we have explored so far.

We need to have courage and confidence to live a life of bold faith.

It's very hard to stick to your Christian principles in a world that often emphasizes the opposite. It's difficult to stay true to God's instruction for our lives when there are temptations all around us that are more popular and acceptable to everyone else. Sometimes you may feel as if you are the only one who steers clear of ungodly activity online or offline, and it can be lonely and isolating when you're trying to remain faithful.

We often witness Christians saying one thing and doing another, or vice versa, and this can be frustrating and confusing. You may have Christian friends who are choosing to behave in ungodly ways either online or offline. You might notice other people in your church who are doing, saying, or sharing things online that go against the Christian principles we are called to honor in our faith. It's especially hard to live a Christian life when you may not be so sure about what you really believe and you're still trying to figure it all out. This is where you must be strong and intentional with prayer, Bible study, and choosing your friends wisely, so you can continue to learn more about Jesus and grow in your faith.

In order to keep growing in your faith and to act with integrity, it's really important to be regularly praying and studying God's Word, while also spending time with other Christians and meeting with a trusted mentor. These four spiritual disciplines are essential to maintaining and growing your faith. Remember this important list, and make sure you stay active in all of these areas:

1. Prayer
2. Studying the Bible
3. Fellowship with other Christians
4. Having a spiritual mentor

The more you grow closer to Christ, the more you will have the desire to be more Christ-like. As you grow in your faith, you will be less tempted to make decisions that are not aligned with God's Word. The more you develop strong relationships centered on Christ, the more you will want to let go of people who regularly make poor choices. The more you pray for guidance and wisdom, the more you will become aware of the various choices that hinder your faith.

Ultimately, the more you walk with the Lord, the more you will love to please Him! The closer you get to Christ, the more you will want to serve Him! And the more you learn about and experience His personal love for you, the more you will want to love Him right back by honoring His instructions and His will for your life.

Scripture Reading and Instruction

Read through the Scripture listed in the following pages about INTEGRITY.

As you read the Bible's instruction on this Christian principle, think through the questions below to get a better understanding of God's Word. Then pick one favorite verse to complete this worksheet.

1. Use your own words to describe what this verse says.

_____

_____

_____

_____

2. What does this verse mean to you?

_____

_____

_____

_____

3. What does this verse teach you?

_____

_____

_____

_____

Biblical Instruction on Integrity

Who is going to harm you if you are eager to do good? But even if you should suffer for what is right, you are blessed. "Do not fear their threats; do not be frightened." But in your hearts revere Christ as Lord. Always be prepared to give an answer to everyone who asks you to give the reason for the hope that you have. But do this with gentleness and respect, keeping a clear conscience, so that those who speak maliciously against your good behavior in Christ may be ashamed of their slander. (1 Peter 3:13-16)

***

I know that you are pleased with me,
for my enemy does not triumph over me.
Because of my integrity you uphold me
and set me in your presence forever. (Psalm 41:11-12)

***

But the fruit of the Spirit is love, joy, peace, forbearance, kindness, goodness, faithfulness, gentleness and self-control. Against such things there is no law. Those who belong to Christ Jesus have crucified the flesh with its passions and desires. Since we live by the Spirit, let us keep in step with the Spirit. (Galatians 5:22-25)

***

The righteous lead blameless lives; blessed are their children after them. (Proverbs 20:7)

***

The integrity of the upright guides them, but the unfaithful are destroyed by their duplicity. (Proverbs 11:3)

***

Teach me, Lord, the way of your decrees,
that I may follow it to the end.
Give me understanding, so that I may keep your law
and obey it with all my heart.

Direct me in the path of your commands,
for there I find delight.
Turn my heart toward your statutes
and not toward selfish gain.

Turn my eyes away from worthless things;
preserve my life according to your word. (Psalm 119:33-37)

Memory Verses

Copy or tear out the following Bible verses for INTEGRITY. Place them somewhere where you can see them every day. Memorize each verse so that God's Word is planted firmly in your heart.

Do not merely listen
to the word,
and so deceive yourselves.
Do what it says.

James 1:22 NIV

Whoever walks in
integrity
walks securely,
but whoever
takes crooked paths
will be found out.

Proverbs 10:9 NIV

Goals and Challenges

1. Identify two general goals you can actively apply online to demonstrate Christian INTEGRITY.

> **GOAL:** I want to be more involved in my youth group and make good Christian friends who will support my faith.

GOAL #1:

_____

GOAL #2:

_____

2. What are the challenges you face in having a Christ-like heart of INTEGRITY online? Identify two specific areas of difficulty and how you will apply this principle of integrity.

> **CHALLENGE:** I don't think God would want me to watch this one particular YouTube channel I like because sometimes it has some inappropriate behavior.
>
> **PRACTICE INTEGRITY BY:** I'm going to stop watching that YouTube channel from now on.

CHALLENGE #1:

_____

PRACTICE INTEGRITY BY:

_____

CHALLENGE #2:

_____

PRACTICE INTEGRITY BY:

_____

Talking Tips

Find a trusted Christian mentor to discuss the answers to the following questions about INTEGRITY with you:

❖ Are there areas in your life where you struggle to practice integrity by upholding your Christian principles? If so, where, and why?

_____

_____

❖ Are you involved in all four areas of Christian activities (mentioned in this chapter) that will support your faith? If not, which ones do you need to pursue? If yes, which ones do you find most helpful?

_____

_____

❖ What really helps you stick to your beliefs? Are there certain friends, Scriptures, or activities that help you the most?

_____

_____

❖ Who are good examples for you to emulate in living a life of Christian integrity? Why are they admirable in this way?

_____

_____

❖ Are you demonstrating Christian integrity every time you go online? Take a good look at what you post, whom you follow, how you interact with others, and where you search online to evaluate your online behavior. Can you share some examples? Where could you do better?

_____

_____

Your Personal Checklist

Think through these questions to help you navigate the online world with a Christ-like heart of INTEGRITY:

- ✓ Have I prayed for God to guide me in practicing my Christian principles?

- ✓ Does what I share online demonstrate Christian integrity?

- ✓ Am I reflecting the heart of Christ when I interact with others online?

- ✓ Is what I see online affecting my commitment to obey God's commands?

- ✓ Am I living out what Christ has taught me?

- ✓ Am I making choices that honor my faith every time I go online?

- ✓ Will people see my Christian values in my online presence?

- ✓ Am I able to discern right from wrong according to biblical truth?

- ✓ Do I follow anyone online who may cause me to veer away from my faith?

- ✓ Am I honoring my Christian values with the people I choose to follow and what I choose to see online?

Prayer

Dear God,
Please guide me in practicing all my Christian principles. Help me make wise decisions that honor You every time my fingers touch the screen. Show me how to be a good representative of Jesus so that others always see You in me.
In Jesus's name, I pray, Amen.

Christian Principle #8:
FAITHFULNESS

Discussion

> But be sure to fear the LORD and serve him faithfully with all your heart; consider what great things he has done for you. (1 Samuel 12:24)

Faithfulness is the result of practicing all of these Christian principles consistently and continually, no matter what challenges we face in our lives. In order to walk closely with the Lord and abide in His truth, we must be regularly reading Scripture while allowing the Holy Spirit to transform our hearts to reflect the character of Christ. We can continue to grow in learning how to love like Jesus, forgive like Jesus, be humble, compassionate, truthful, and wise through every season of our lives, ultimately living a life of Christian integrity while demonstrating these principles. Our God is forever faithful to us, and we must strive to honor His love and enduring faithfulness by returning that same love and faithfulness to Him. He has great plans for our lives if we stay faithful and trust in Him.

> "For I know the plans I have for you," declares the LORD, "plans to prosper you and not to harm you, plans to give you hope and a future." (Jeremiah 29:11)

Our faithfulness will be tested throughout our entire lives. As you grow older, there will always be new experiences, ideas, lifestyle choices, and opinions you will learn about that may challenge you in remaining faithful. Sometimes you will have to make difficult decisions in order to honor God. You might face a lot of pressure from your friends to act in a certain way that goes against your Christian principles, both offline and online. It can be tempting to go along with the "norm" in order to continue to fit in and be liked, but please pray for strength to resist doing anything that interferes with your relationship with Christ.

> Trust in the LORD forever,
> for the LORD, the LORD himself, is the Rock eternal. (Isaiah 26:4)

The more you stay faithful to your Christian principles, the more you will grow in your faith!

Closely follow the examples of Christians you know who remain faithful so that you can watch and learn from them. Remind yourself regularly that the things of this world aren't as important as the things of eternity in Heaven. What might seem so important to you now will probably fade, but God's Word lives forever. Your relationship with Him will go far beyond the choice you are facing, the experience you are wanting, and this season you are in. God's instructions for us to live faithful lives are all given to protect us from sinful situations that can cause us harm. If you've ever made a big mistake, you know how it feels. Of course, we all will make mistakes, but the closer you walk with the Lord, the more you will be strengthened to remain faithful in honoring Him with your words and actions. This will help you to steer clear of opportunities that could get you in trouble.

> "Therefore, everyone who hears these words of mine and puts them into practice is like a wise man who built his house on the rock. The rain came down, the streams rose, and the winds blew and beat against that house; yet it did not fall, because it had its foundation on the rock. But everyone who hears these words of mine and does not put them into practice is like a foolish man who built his house on sand. The rain came down, the streams rose, and the winds blew and beat against that house, and it fell with a great crash." (Matthew 7:24-27)

There is no perfect committed Christian, so always trust in a gracious God who forgives and renews your heart for Him every day.

As you try to remain faithful and true to God's will for your life, there will be many opportunities for you to fail, to fumble, to make wrong decisions, and even to turn away from God. Being faithful is a long, hard road, and no one gets it right all of the time. No matter what you do or how badly you fail, always remember that God is a God of *grace,* for His mercies never end. That means He will never stop loving you no matter what you do. When you are able to acknowledge what you did wrong and ask for His forgiveness (repent), it is through Christ you are washed clean of your sins. Keep trying your best, and continue to pray that God will help you grow closer to Him.

> If we confess our sins, he is faithful and just and will forgive us our sins and purify us from all unrighteousness. (1 John 1:9)

The stronger your foundation of faith grows, the more fulfilling your life will be! If you continue to develop a Christ-like heart and pursue God through prayer, fellowship, and studying Scripture, you will experience deep meaning in your life. Knowing you are God's beloved child and living your life anchored to His promises will bring you assurance you were created for a purpose by your loving Creator. You will find comfort in knowing Christ is *in you* and *with you* through every hard situation, painful circumstance, and incredible accomplishment, too. You are *never* alone.

When you experience hardship and pain, trust that God is at work to make something good out of your situation and that He will heal your hurt.

God never wants us to suffer, but this world is full of pain, and you will surely experience it. No matter what you are going through, God is deeply aware of your circumstance and feels great anguish when His children are struggling. He only wants good things for you, and He longs to comfort you and guide you every step of the way.

Trust in the Lord with all your heart
Lean not on your own understanding;
In all your ways submit to him,
And he will make your paths straight. (Proverbs 3:5-6)

Sometimes the hardest thing to do is to trust in His goodness and His plans for your life, but that is where faith is practiced at its fullest.

Keep reaching to Him in times of trouble! Even when you don't see any hope or help in sight, I promise He is caring for you in ways you may not yet see or understand. Sometimes you will see evidence of God in your circumstances, but at other times, you may not see it until much later. God uses everything we experience for a greater purpose in our lives. Some of the hardest struggles we endure become the launching ground for something incredible, and He uses that struggle to prepare us for it! Keep praying, reading His Word, and reaching out to other Christians for support when you are going through a difficult time.

> And we know that in all things God works for the good of those who love him, who have been called according to his purpose. (Romans 8:28)

Scripture Reading and Instruction

Read through the Scripture listed in the following pages about FAITHFULNESS.

As you read the Bible's instruction on this Christian principle, think through the questions below to get a better understanding of God's Word. Then pick one favorite verse to complete this worksheet.

1. Use your own words to describe what this verse says.

_____

_____

_____

_____

2. What does this verse mean to you?

_____

_____

_____

_____

3. What does this verse teach you?

_____

_____

_____

_____

Biblical Instruction on Faithfulness

Know therefore that the LORD your God is God; he is the faithful God, keeping his covenant of love to a thousand generations of those who love him and keep his commandments. (Deuteronomy 7:9)

***

For great is his love toward us,
and the faithfulness of the LORD endures forever.
Praise the LORD. (Psalm 117:2)

***

Now faith is confidence in what we hope for and assurance about what we do not see. (Hebrews 11:1)

***

And pray in the Spirit on all occasions with all kinds of prayers and requests. With this in mind, be alert and always keep on praying for all the Lord's people. (Ephesians 6:18)

***

Blessed is the one
who does not walk in step with the wicked
or stand in the way that sinners take
or sit in the company of mockers,
but whose delight is in the law of the LORD,
and who meditates on his law day and night. (Psalm 1:1-2)

***

No temptation has overtaken you except what is common to mankind. And God is faithful; he will not let you be tempted beyond what you can bear. But when you are tempted, he will also provide a way out so that you can endure it. (1 Corinthians 10:13)

***

Therefore, my dear brothers and sisters, stand firm. Let nothing move you. Always give yourselves fully to the work of the Lord, because you know that your labor in the Lord is not in vain. (1 Corinthians 15:58)

***

Rejoice always, pray continually, give thanks in all circumstances; for this is God's will for you in Christ Jesus. (1 Thessalonians 5:16-18)

Memory Verses

Copy or tear out the following Bible verses for FAITHFULNESS. Place them somewhere where you can see them every day. Memorize each verse so that God's Word is planted firmly in your heart.

For the Lord
is good and his love
endures forever;
his faithfulness
continues through all
the generations.

Psalm 100:5 NIV

The Lord is my rock, my
fortress, and my deliverer;
my God is my rock, in whom
I take refuge, my shield and
the horn of my salvation, my
stronghold.

Psalm 18:2 NIV

Goals and Challenges

1. Identify two general goals you can actively apply online to demonstrate Christian FAITHFULNESS.

> **GOAL:** I'm going to stop following people on social media who share inappropriate content.

GOAL #1:

_____

GOAL #2:

_____

2. What are the challenges you face in having a Christ-like heart of FAITHFULNESS online? Identify two specific areas of difficulty and how you will apply this principle of FAITHFULNESS.

> **CHALLENGE:** When I'm in a bad mood, I'm tempted to make sinful choices online.

> **APPLY FAITHFULNESS BY:** When I feel tempted to sin online, I will get off my phone, pray for strength to not sin, and reach out to my Christian friends for support.

CHALLENGE #1:

_____

APPLY FAITHFULNESS BY:

_____

CHALLENGE #2:

_____

APPLY FAITHFULNESS BY:

_____

Talking Tips

Find a trusted Christian mentor to discuss the answers to the following questions about FAITHFULNESS with you:

❖ Out of all the Christian principles discussed, which ones are the hardest for you to practice in your life and online? Why do you think that is?

_____

_____

❖ What are some ways you can grow and receive support in those areas?

_____

_____

❖ When you are going through difficult circumstances, what are some active steps you can take to stay faithful?

_____

_____

❖ Who in your life exemplifies faithfulness? What do they do that makes you believe they are living out their faith so well?

_____

_____

❖ Are there specific things/people/activities you need to eliminate or add to your life to practice faithfulness more successfully? List them, then add them to your goal sheet.

_____

_____

Your Personal Checklist

Think through these questions to help you navigate the online world with a Christ-like heart of FAITHFULNESS:

- ✓ Have I prayed about how God wants me to behave online?

- ✓ Does this post, picture, or message challenge my faith in any way?

- ✓ Have I searched Scripture for wisdom on topics I don't understand?

- ✓ Do I trust that God wants what is best for me?

- ✓ Am I sticking to my Christian values every time I go online?

- ✓ Do I ask my Christian friends/spiritual mentors/parents for guidance on a regular basis?

- ✓ Am I trusting in God's plan and purpose for my life even when I am going through difficult times?

- ✓ What are some new ways I can continue to grow my faith?

- ✓ Am I measuring my worth through my friends' and the media's opinion or through God's view of me?

- ✓ When I make mistakes, do I repent and learn from my experience?

Prayer

Dear God,
I want to be faithful to You in all circumstances, so please help me trust in Your plan for my life. Show me what I need to work on in my faith, and guide me as I grow in those areas. Help me to stay close to You and to feel Your presence in my life every day.
In Jesus's name, I pray, Amen.

Good Guidelines for Appropriate Screen Time

Before we wrap this up, I want to address one more very important issue:

How much time should you be spending on your phone?

Here's the thing about that.

First and foremost, your parents make that decision. Period. It doesn't matter how you feel about their rules because they are your parents and you need to trust that they know what is best for you, okay? Also, you need to obey them because God said so. It's right there in the Ten Commandments.

> "Honor your father and your mother, so that you may live long in the land the LORD your God is giving you." (Exodus 20:12)

With that said, whenever you are on your phone, I have some guidelines that might be helpful in deciding the amount of appropriate screen time. It's important that you develop a good, secure system of limit-setting for time spent on your phone because everyone (yes, adults, too) needs this. The digital world is both marvelous and menacing to our health. Too much of it—like too much of anything—is never good for you, so it's really important you learn how to manage it responsibly now. There are two categories of screen time I want to identify:

1. Appropriate and useful screen time is time spent online that is valuable to you, your health, your faith, your mind, your friendships, and your family. This screen time is spent doing the following:

- Communicating with parents
- Connecting with friends/family
- Doing homework/studying for tests
- Researching information on important topics of interest
- Listening to motivational music/praise and worship music
- Watching sermons online
- Looking up Bible verses, ministries, mission trips, etc.
- Reading Christian devotionals, blogs, or books
- Investigating future career or college opportunities
- Participating in online study groups or online fellowship

2. Not-so-useful but fun and entertaining screen time is time spent on your screens that isn't considered valuable to your mental or physical health; these activities do not nourish your faith. This screen time is spent doing the following:

- Scrolling through social media
- Watching TV shows or movies
- Viewing music or YouTube videos
- Playing video games
- Texting/messaging with friends about random things
- Surfing the web looking for entertainment
- Shopping
- Looking at Pinterest for ideas
- Watching DIY videos, or looking up recipes, home décor, hair or make-up tutorials, etc.
- Reading the latest celebrity news

So, let's use some common sense here. The first type of screen time is the most productive and valuable to you, so of course spending more time doing those online activities can be both beneficial and useful!

On the other hand, the second example of screen time is simply fun and entertaining. Certainly, we all enjoy having that in our lives! There's nothing wrong with using your phone for these activities, but when we spend too much screen time in this second category, we are not pursuing all that God wants us to be. We are poorly managing our time and missing out on activities of greater value to us. We have fallen into the trap of distraction, which greatly interferes with our lives.

Sometimes our screen time takes over our lives and we lose sight of the most important priorities we should have in place. This can be very damaging and dangerous! Don't use screen time to distract you from the real elements of your life that need attention. Some days you might even enjoy being online more than being in the real world. Sometimes it's easy to use it as an escape from the hard tasks you need to do. However, using your phone as a means of distraction or procrastination from important life experiences is surely not what God wants for you. He made you to interact with the real world because human contact is a necessity. In order for you to develop your God-given gifts and live a productive life, you need to set limits on this type of screen time.

You can do this by setting a specific amount of time every day for this type of phone use. There are many apps that can help you do this and many ways in which you can make this a good habit. You can also set an alarm for when you need to go offline to focus on your real-life responsibilities. This self-discipline is one of the most important life skills you can learn.

Your phone can be a wonderful way to grow in your faith and practice Christian principles. It can be a fantastic tool for connecting with other people and learning more about this world and all the gifts it has to offer you. And yet, your phone can also interfere with your ability to do life the way God wants you to, so please take your screen time seriously and practice self-control.

A Word of Caution: When you are navigating the online world, please make safe choices in whom you interact with and where you go. Do not engage with strangers, and never give out any of your personal information. On the internet, there are dangerous people who have malicious intentions, and they often pose as someone other than themselves. You do ***not*** have the ability to know who they are behind the screen, so never interact with anyone you do not know personally. Please don't blindly trust people you don't know who contact you because, sadly, you can't trust them. Be extremely careful with your choices, and if anyone approaches you that you do not know, don't respond; immediately block that person. Do not believe what they say! If you can't seem to block them or stop them from interacting with you, then you must tell an adult who can intervene.

Conclusion

These Christian principles are so important to understand and practice as you grow in your faith. What we do both offline and online reveals who we are and what we believe. Remember all that you learned so you can continue to grow in your faith through all the ways we talked about in this guide.

When you grow closer to Christ, you will gain more strength and understanding, more courage and confidence in who you are as a beloved child of God. When we feel wholly loved by our Creator and believe that He wants the very best for us, we are comforted and encouraged to walk with the Lord every day and extend His grace and love to others. Best of all, we can be assured that no matter how hard life gets, God is with us every step of the way. When you are discouraged and don't feel like you can handle whatever challenge you are facing, always know that with Christ, you can do *all* things. It still may be hard, but He will give you the strength you need.

> I can do all this through him who gives me strength. (Philippians 4:13)

When you are online, wherever you go and whatever you do, you will be faced with many decisions about how to behave in a Christ-like manner. I pray that you will experience God's presence and guidance as you take those faithful steps forward and trust in His will for your life.

And always remember: You were created *on purpose for a purpose*, so allow God to help you grow into the *very best you* He designed you to be, okay? I promise, He always knows best.

Tear out or copy the master checklist and prayer for whenever you need Christian guidance. Fold them up, and tuck them into your phone case so that you can refer to them whenever needed.

Master Checklist for Sticking to Your Christian Principles

- Am I interacting on social media in a Christ-like way?

- Am I loving others the way Christ loves me?

- Am I able to offer forgiveness when someone offends me?

- Am I able to acknowledge my mistakes and ask forgiveness from others?

- Does what I share on social media come across as arrogant or selfish?

- Am I being compassionate when I see that someone is hurting?

- If I see something negative happening online, am I intervening in a Christ-like way?

- Am I being respectful to *all* people when I engage online?

- When I see something I don't understand, am I seeking a trusted mentor?

- Am I discerning what is true or not true when I read content online?

- If I see anything dangerous online, am I alerting an adult or authority figure?

- Am I being honest and positive when I engage on social media?

- Are the people I am following online helping or hindering my faith?

- Do I stay away from sites that can be inappropriate and damaging to my faith?

- Am I sharing my faith with those who are interested in what I believe?

- Am I reaching out to friends and inviting them to church, youth group, or Bible studies?

- Am I managing my screen time responsibly?

Dear God,

I want to honor You every time I get online. Please guide me in all my decisions and show me how to reflect the heart of Christ in everything I post and everywhere I go. Help me grow closer to You and draw on Your love and grace so I can extend both to others.

Show me all the ways I can focus on people's needs and be more compassionate and less prideful. Teach me the best ways to resolve conflicts and manage difficult situations I experience. Fill me with Your wisdom to discern right from wrong according to Your Word, and give me the strength to stay faithful no matter how tempted I am to stray.

I know the internet can be dangerous, so I ask for Your protection and direction, and I promise to be mindful of sites and strangers I shouldn't trust. I'm so grateful for Your love that never fails even when I do. I want to trust in Your plan for my life and to believe that I am uniquely designed for that purpose. Fill me with Your light, so others always see You shining in me.

In Jesus's name, I pray, Amen.

If you appreciated
Follow Jesus: A Christian Teen's Guide to Navigating the Online World,
kindly consider leaving a review at *Amazon* or *Goodreads*.

You won't want to miss Christine Carter's first book:

Help and Hope While You're Healing:
A Woman's Guide Toward Wellness While Recovering from Injury, Surgery, or Illness.

Christine would love to connect with you in the following ways:

The Mom Café Blog
www.themomcafe.com

Twitter
@themomcafe
twitter.com/themomcafe

Facebook
facebook.com/TheMomCafe/

Pinterest
pinterest.com/themomcafe/

Email
Chris@TheMomCafe.com

Updates on future publications can be found at:

GROUND TRUTH PRESS
P.O. Box 7313
Nashua, NH 03060-7313

www.groundtruthpress.com

Made in the USA
San Bernardino, CA
08 May 2019